THE GREAT INDIA CHALLENGE

Vinita Zutshi's fascination with words led to her becoming a writer. She enjoys writing both fiction and non-fiction for children and adults, and has created innovative formats in personalised writing. *The Great India Challenge* was born from her daughter's enchantment with social sciences—and Vinita's ignorance of it!

Find out more about Vinita's work on www.penchanteur.com. You can contact Vinita at vinita@penchanteur.com

for Jai, with love

Published by Scholastic India Pvt. Ltd.
A subsidiary of Scholastic Inc., New York, 10012 (USA).
Publishers since 1920, with international operations in Canada,
Australia, New Zealand, the United Kingdom, India, and Hong Kong.

For information regarding permission, write to:
Scholastic India Pvt. Ltd.
A-27, Ground Floor, Sigma Centre
Infocity-1, Sector 34, Gurgaon-122001 (India)

First edition: February 2011
This reprint edition: November 2025

ISBN-13: 978-81-8477-666-9

Printed at Saurabh Printers Pvt.Ltd

The Great India Challenge

Puzzles, Quizzes and Games

Vinita Zutshi

Illustrations by Priya Kuriyan

SCHOLASTIC

New York Toronto London Auckland
Sydney New Delhi Hong Kong

Contents

Arts & Culture 37

Music & Movies 47

All Creatures Great and Small 53

Food for Thought 57

All Things Indian 63

Answers 71

Historic India

Father of Our Nation

How familiar are you with the story of Mahatma Gandhi's life? Find out by naming the locations in which these incidents took place.

1. He was born here: _ _ _ _ _ _ _ _ _
2. He went to school here: _ _ _ _ _ _
3. He joined college here : _ _ _ _ _ _ _ _ _
4. He studied law here: _ _ _ _ _ _
5. He first attempted to establish a law practice here: _ _ _ _ _ _
6. He was the first Indian to be enrolled as the Advocate of the Supreme Court here in South Africa: _ _ _ _ _
7. He founded the Sabarmati Ashram here: _ _ _ _ _ _ _ _ _
8. The massacre of Indians meeting peacefully here in Punjab and the violence that followed gave rise to the idea of *swaraj* in his mind:
   _ _ _ _ _ _ _ _
9. He began the boycott of foreign cloth here: _ _ _ _ _ _
10. He called off the campaign of mass civil disobedience after a violent clash in this town in Uttar Pradesh: _ _ _ _ _ _   _ _ _ _ _ _
11. He broke the salt law by marching to this place and picking up salt:
    _ _ _ _ _
12. He was assassinated here: _ _ _ _ _

Answers on page 72

2 India Reformed

Solve the clues given below and complete the names of some famous social reformers of India.

1. _ _ _ _ _YA (the Hindi word for 'pickle') _ _ _ _ BA (the Italian word for 'wine') B_ _ _ _ (to own or hold something)

2. _ _ _ _ (one of the Indian words for 'father') AM _ _ (the first two letters of the word for a hot, refreshing beverage, popular in India)

3. DR BR _ _ _ _ _ KAR (first two letters: it rhymes with the word for a male sheep; next three letters: we sleep on it)

4. ISH _ _ _ (the opposite of peace) C _ _ _ _ RA (we hold a pencil with this part of our body) VIDYA _ _ _ _ _ (the Hindi word for 'sea')

5. SHRI _ _ _ A _ _ _ _ _ _ _ (first three letters: the husband of Sita; last seven letters: an avatar of Vishnu) PA _ _ _ AHANSA (repeat the answer to the first clue)

6. _ _ _ _ _ _ _ (first five letters: the Hindi word for 'light'; last two letters: the Gujarati word for 'mother') PHULE

7. _ _ _ _ ER (the less popular cousin of the butterfly) T _ _ _ SA (a poetic way of saying 'before')

8. ANNIE _ _ _ _ _T (the Hindi word for flour made from chickpeas)

9. SWAMI _ _ _ ANAND (the opposite of 'night') _ _ _ _ _ _ _ _ _ _ (the goddess of knowledge)

10. _ _ _ _ (the Hindi word for 'king') RAM _ _ _ AN (the reverse of the first three letters of what we call the house in which we live) ROY

Answers on page 72

3 The Presidential Seal

Match the names of former Presidents of India in Column A with pieces of information about them in Column B.

Column A	Column B
R Venkataraman	Missile Man of India
Dr Rajendra Prasad	Teachers' Day is celebrated on his birthday
Giani Zail Singh	India's first woman President
Dr Fakhruddin Ali Ahmed	was awarded the Bharat Ratna
Dr Sarvapalli Radhakrishnan	established Jamia Millia Islamia
Dr APJ Abdul Kalam	served as Chief Minister of Punjab
Pratibha Devisingh Patil	swore in three Prime Ministers in one year
Dr VV Giri	first Chief Minister of Andhra Pradesh
KR Narayanan	was a delegate to the UN General Assembly
Dr Zakir Hussain	India's first President
Neelam Sanjiva Reddy	served as India's Ambassador to the USA
Shankar Dayal Sharma	died while in office

Answers on page 72

Words of Wisdom

Solve the clues below and fill in the blanks. Copy each numbered letter onto a blank with the same number at the bottom of the page. Once you are done, you will have a famous quote and the name of the legendary Indian personality who is known to have said it.

Clue	Blanks
a liquid necessary to sustain life	_ _ _ _ _ 1 2 3 4 5
a primary colour	_ _ _ _ 6 7 8 4
you would find a cross in this place of worship	_ _ _ _ _ _ 9 10 8 11 9 10
man's best friend	_ _ _ 12 13 14
'plus' or 'minus' in Maths	_ _ _ _ 15 16 14 17
another word for 'possibly'	_ _ _ _ _ 18 2 19 6 4

'_ _   _ _ _   _ _ _ _ _ _   _ _ _   _ _ _ _   _ _   _ _ _

6 4   3 10 4   9 10 2 17 14 4   19 13 8   1 16 15 10   3 13   15 4 4

_ _   _ _ _   _ _ _ _ _' – _ _ _ _ _ _ _   _ _ _ _ _ _

16 17   3 10 4   1 13 11 7 12   18 2 10 2 3 18 2   14 2 17 12 10 16

Answers on page 73

5

Ancient Times

Join two letter-groups from the box below to make six-letter words that are answers to the clues given on the page. Strike off a letter-group once you have used it. Write the words top down in the grid. When you have filled the grid, you will be able to read across the starred rows the names of two ancient Indian cities.

SES	LET	HEI	PUL	UAL	UNE	AMU
IMM	GHT	GHS	LET	NEI	TAB	ANN

	1	2	3	4	5	6	7
city 1	*	*	*	*	*	*	*
city 2	*	*	*	*	*	*	*

Clues:

1. seeds of legumes

2. worn as a charm against evil

3. that cannot be harmed by disease

4. a small and hard piece of medicine

5. measure of how tall a person is

6. happening every year

7. sounds made by a horse

Answers on page 73

6

Hold the Fort

Place a letter-pair from the box below in each of the spaces provided to end the name of a person and begin the name of a fort in India. Strike off each letter-pair as you use it.

RA	AM	JA	FA
PU	CH	JU	MU
GO	LA	SH	ME

KOKI|___|L QILA

NEEL|___|BER

MAN|___|NAGADH

SALO|___|HRANGARH

ENO|___|ITTORGARH

SHAILA|___|ISALMER

PAP|___|RANA QILA

SAMEE|___|NTHAMBORE

MAR|___|LCONDA

MUSTA|___|TEHPUR SIKRI

SURE|___|ANIWAR WADA

RA|___|RUD-JANJIRA

Answers on page 73

Heritage Sites

Given below are the names of various UNESCO world heritage sites in India. Match each site with the state in which it is located.

UNESCO World Heritage Site	State
1. Mahabodhi Temple Complex	a. Tamil Nadu
2. Humayun's Tomb	b. Karnataka
3. Champaner-Pavagadh Archaeological Park	c. West Bengal
4. Group of monuments at Hampi	d. Delhi
5. Rock shelters at Bhimbetka	e. Himachal Pradesh
6. Nilgiri Mountain Railway	f. Uttarakhand
7. Ajanta caves	g. Bihar
8. Keoladeo National Park	h. Madhya Pradesh
9. Manas Wildlife sanctuary	i. Maharashtra
10. Agra Fort	j. Gujarat
11. Valley of Flowers	k. Uttar Pradesh
12. Sundarbans	l. Orissa
13. Kalka-Shimla Railway	m. Rajasthan
14. Sun Temple	n. Assam

Answers on page 73

8 Words of Wisdom 2

Solve the clues below and fill in the blanks. Copy each numbered letter onto a blank with the same number at the bottom of the page. Once you are done, you will have a famous saying and the name of the legendary Indian personality who said it.

a pair of small drums played with the hands

_ _ _ _ _
1 2 3 4 2

this kind of bird is ugly in a popular fairy tale

_ _ _ _ _ _ _ _
5 6 7 8 4 9 10 11

a colour obtained by mixing black and white

_ _ _ _
11 12 13 14

a spectacle or display

_ _ _ _
15 16 17 18

another word for 'film'

_ _ _ _ _
19 17 20 9 13

'_ _ _   _ _ _ _ _   _ _   _ _ _   _ _ _ _ _
1 16 13   18 17 12 4 5   9 15   1 16 13   11 12 13 2 1

_ _ _ _ _ _ _ _ _   _ _ _ _ _   _ _   _ _ _ _   _ _
11 14 19 10 2 15 9 6 19   18 16 13 12 13   18 13   7 17 19 13   1 17

_ _ _ _   _ _ _ _ _ _ _ _ _   _ _ _ _ _ _'
19 2 8 13   17 6 12 15 13 4 20 13 15   15 1 12 17 10 11

– _ _ _ _ _   _ _ _ _ _ _ _ _ _ _ _ _
15 18 2 19 9   20 9 20 13 8 2 10 2 10 5 2

Answers on page 73

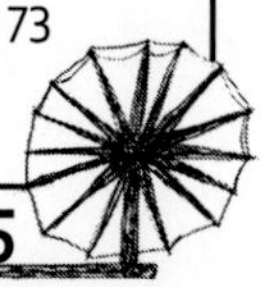

Around the Country in 20 Puzzles

9

Matters of State

Identify the name of a state of India by inserting the names of cities and towns located in that state into the grid in alphabetical order. Read down the starred column once you are done.

*

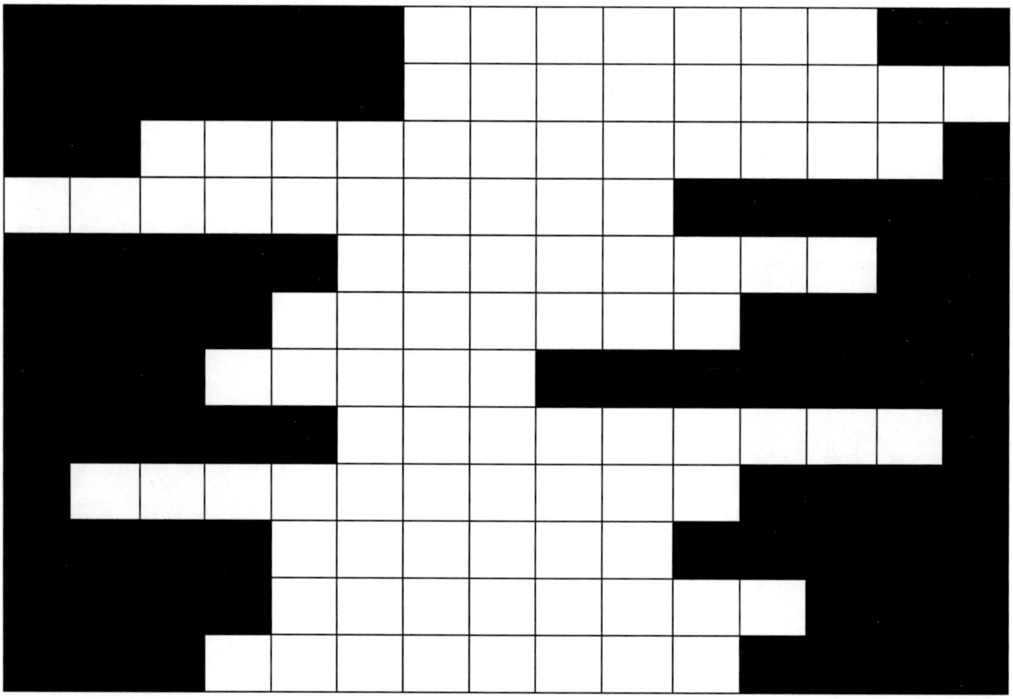

Kusumkasa Dhondhatarai Satrenga Malkangiri Chitrakot Dongargaon Karsi Singhora Hattigam Achhota Kanteli Palaud

Answers on page 74

10

Call a City by a New Name

The names of several cities and towns in India have changed over time. Match the old name of each city in Column A with its new name in Column B.

Column A	Column B
Quilon	Thrissoor
Benares	Vadodara
Madras	Kochi
Bombay	Kolkata
Trivandrum	Kodagu
Baroda	Varanasi
Calicut	Chennai
Cochin	Thiruvananthapuram
Calcutta	Mumbai
Trichur	Kollam
Coorg	Kozhikode

Answers on page 74

11

District-wise

The names of some Indian districts have been listed below. Place each name in the middle of a word box so that you have five three-letter words when you read the letters top down. Two district names from the list cannot be used. Which are they?

TUMKUR HAVERI KOPPAL MANDYA HASSAN
YADGIR KODAGU

S T S A B A
_ _ _ _ _ _
Y N Y E T E

I B O A D R
_ _ _ _ _ _
P N E D E G

S S A A S A
_ _ _ _ _ _
E P K H T T

B C O A F A
_ _ _ _ _ _
E D E E R K

T C E H C S
_ _ _ _ _ _
Y N E N Y N

Answers on page 74

Mountains to Climb

Solve the clues in each of the two puzzle sets below to make common five-letter words. Read the letter inserted into each group bottom up to find the names of two mountain ranges in India.

Scarlett O Hara had a very thin one	WA__ST
A little too bright	LU__ID
This is how you move when you don't want to be seen	SL__NK
An old-fashioned bet	WA__ER
A distinguishing feature of birds of prey	TA__ON
One of the most ancient forms of money	CO__N

A long, thick curtain	DR__PE
We feel this when there is absolutely nothing to do	BO__ED
If you were a clown, this is what you would do for a loving	AM__SE
A famous musician who drove rats away from Hamelin	PI__ER
The first five letters of the name of a well-loved comic book character	AS__ER
When you take a risk, you put certain things at this place	ST__KE
A must-eat if you go to Japan	SU__HI

Answers on page 75

13

A River is the Sum of its Parts

Below is a list of names of the tributaries of a major Indian river. Strike out these names from the grid. You will be left with the letters in the name of the river and the name of a dam built across it. Unscramble the letters and write the names in the blanks at the bottom of the page.

H	O	N	N	U	H	O	L	E	T
E	I	K	S	K	A	V	E	I	A
M	N	A	H	R	I	K	R	R	N
A	A	P	I	I	S	T	I	H	A
V	V	I	M	N	H	N	A	R	M
A	A	L	S	A	I	A	J	A	H
T	H	A	H	B	S	A	G	A	S
I	B	L	A	Y	Y	O	N	R	K
A	R	K	A	V	A	T	H	Y	A
I	N	A	V	A	P	A	K	O	L

SHIMSHA TIRTHA ARKAVATHY

KAPILA HONNUHOLE LAKSHMANA

KABINI LOKAPAVANI BHAVANI

NOYYAL HEMAVATI

Name of the river: ______________________

Name of the dam across the river: ______________________

Answers on page 75

14

Fruity Places

Solve the clues below and identify the names of some common and uncommon Indian fruits. Complete the names of Indian towns and cities by using the first three letters of each fruit.

Example: This brown fruit is fleshy and round, and has large black seeds which cannot be eaten. ___ ___ ___ K M A G A L U R

Answer: Fruit—Chikoo City—Chikmagalur

1. Available in summer, this is considered the king of fruits.
   ___ ___ ___ G A L O R E
2. Monkeys love to eat this long fruit. ___ ___ ___ S W A R A
3. This purplish-black fruit with large seeds is available during the monsoons and can colour the tongue purple. ___ ___ ___ N A G A R
4. The water inside this fruit makes for a cool refreshing drink. ___ ___ ___ H I N
5. This delicious, red fruit grows in Himachal Pradesh and Kashmir.
   ___ ___ ___ R A P U N J I
6. These juicy, red or yellow fleshy fruits are eaten during summer.
   ___ ___ ___ UR
7. Deep yellow in colour, it has a delicious taste and is similar in appearance to the uncut jackfruit. ___ ___ ___ G A P U R
8. This fruit is consumed in dried form, as a juice and as a sauce.
   ___ ___ ___ N G A N O R E

Answers on page 75

15 City Slickers

Use the hints given in brackets to complete the names of some Indian cities and states.

1. (that girl) KURUK ___ ___ ___TRA
2. (crazy) ___ ___ ___URAI
3. (moved fast on foot) VA ___ ___ ___ASI
4. (jump and leap on one foot) B ___ ___ ___AL
5. (cricket equipment) COIM ___ ___ ___ORE
6. (use scissors) CALI ___ ___ ___
7. (male sheep) DHA ___ ___ ___SALA
8. (drawings, paintings and sculpture) AG ___ ___ ___ALA
9. (found in an atlas) DI ___ ___ ___UR
10. (not her) KO ___ ___ ___A

Answers on page 75

16 Going 'Bad'

Solve the clues given below to find the names of some 'bad' Indian cities.

1. Capital of Andhra Pradesh ________________
2. City in Uttar Pradesh where the Kumbh Mela is held ________________
3. Located on the banks of the River Sabarmati in Gujarat ________________
4. City in Maharashtra named after Emperor Aurangzeb ________________
5. City in Uttar Pradesh famous for its glass and bangle works ____________

Answers on page 76

17

On the Road

Use the clues given to unscramble the names of some Indian cities. Rewrite the letters in the boxes to find the name of one of South Asia's oldest and longest roads.

1. RUDURGAP—a city in West Bengal famous for its steel plant
   _ _ _ ☐ _ _ _ _
2. GABARDUNAA—a city named after the son of Emperor Shah Jahan
   _ _ ☐ _ _ _ _ _ _ _
3. LOSSAAN—a coal mining and industrial city in West Bengal
   _ _ ☐ _ _ _ _
4. SARAVANI—a city in Uttar Pradesh on the banks of the River Ganga
   _ _ _ _ ☐ _ _ _
5. DABANDH—a city in Jharkhand famous for its mines _ _ _ _ _ _ ☐
6. MARASTIR—the city with the Golden Temple _ _ _ _ ☐ _ _ _
7. HAGARLI—a city in UP famous for its university _ _ _ _ _ ☐ _
8. ALUHIDAN—a city in Punjab famous for its hosiery and woollens
   _ ☐ _ _ _ _ _ _
9. DAHAJALRN—a city in Punjab that is a major supplier of sports goods
   _ _ _ _ ☐ _ _ _ _
10. AKATOLK—the Howrah Bridge is located in this city _ _ _ ☐ _ _ _

_ _ _ _ _   _ _ _ _ _ ROAD

Answers on page 76

18

Mountain Meadows

In the puzzle sets below, find the first letter of each word using the clues given. Once you are done, read the first letters top down and you will have the names of three meadows in the Pir Panjal range in Kashmir.

__ NIFE (instrument for cutting)

__ BODE (place to stay)

__ IGHT (not day)

__ REEN (colour found in nature)

__ ATER (liquid that sustains life)

__ GAIN (once more)

__ ABLE (you pull a chair up to it)

__ PPLE (it keeps the doctor away)

__ EVER (not ever)

____

__ AMB (a baby sheep)

__ MBRELLA (keeps the rain away)

__ ESERT (a place full of sand)

__ PPER (not lower)

__ AVEN (a black bird)

__ ENU (a bill of fare)

__ RMY (too many ants)

__ IGHT (we don't drive on this side of the road

__ ARAGE (a place to park the car)

____

__ OOD (not bad)

__ GLY (a famous duckling is described as this)

__ ISTEN (teachers tell us to do this)

__ ARKET (where people go to buy things)

__ LIEN (a being from another planet)

__ IVER (a water body)

__ UEST (visitor at your home)

____

Answers on page 76

19 Read Between the Letters

Each name in the first column below contains a word that is an answer to the clue in column two. Find the word by striking out the extra letters and write it in the Answer column.

Example: ~~K~~ A ~~L A H A~~ N D ~~I~~   a word that joins   AND

City	Clue	Answer
1. NAGPUR	short sleep	
2. VIJAYWADA	bone structure that holds our teeth	
3. KURUKSHETRA	reddish-brown substance that forms on metal	
4. ITANAGAR	the colour of skin when it is exposed to the sun	
5. PORBANDAR	animal that feeds on bamboo shoots	
6. RISHIKESH	a dangerous chance	
7. LUCKNOW	not high	
8. PATHANKOT	a large container used to store liquid or gas	
9. BANGALORE	it can be acute, right or obtuse	
10. BIKANER	two-wheeled vehicle	
11. COIMBATORE	armed fighting	
12. FARIDKOT	Noah built one	
13. DARJEELING	jewellery for the fingers	
14. BELGAUM	we chew this	

Answers on page 76

20

Changing Districts

Given below are the names of some Indian districts. With each name, change one letter at a time to form a word in the English language. Keep changing till you get to the word at the end.

Example: PALI is a district, and it needs to be changed to get the word ROLL.

PAL~~I~~ ⟶ *PAL~~E~~* ⟶ *~~P~~ALL* ⟶ *T~~A~~LL* ⟶ *~~T~~OLL* ⟶ ***ROLL***

PURI

_ _ _ _

_ _ _ _

_ _ _ _

_ _ _ _

SOLD

GAYA

_ _ _ _

_ _ _ _

_ _ _ _

_ _ _ _

BOLT

PUNE

_ _ _ _

_ _ _ _

_ _ _ _

_ _ _ _

JARS

BEED

_ _ _ _

_ _ _ _

_ _ _ _

_ _ _ _

LOAN

TONK

_ _ _ _

_ _ _ _

_ _ _ _

_ _ _ _

PARE

JIND

_ _ _ _

_ _ _ _

_ _ _ _

_ _ _ _

MATE

Answers on page 77

Changing Rivers

Given below are the names of some Indian rivers. With each name, change one letter at a time to form a word in the English language. Keep changing till you reach the word at the end.

Example: Start with SON and end with REP.

~~S~~ON ⟶ T~~O~~N ⟶ ~~T~~EN ⟶ PE~~N~~ ⟶ ~~P~~EP ⟶ ***REP***

RAVI	MAHI	BEAS
_ _ _ _	_ _ _ _	_ _ _ _
_ _ _ _	_ _ _ _	_ _ _ _
_ _ _ _	_ _ _ _	_ _ _ _
_ _ _ _	_ _ _ _	_ _ _ _
LOST	TUGS	TOLD

TAPI	BORI	SAGI
_ _ _ _	_ _ _ _	_ _ _ _
_ _ _ _	_ _ _ _	_ _ _ _
_ _ _ _	_ _ _ _	_ _ _ _
_ _ _ _	_ _ _ _	_ _ _ _
LETS	TASK	HOLD

Answers on page 77

22

Q Up

Strike off the words in the list below from the grid vertically (upward and downward), horizontally (forward and backward), and diagonally. Read the remaining letters across each row to find the name of a town in India that starts with the letter Q.

Q	Q	Q	U	A	I	L	Q	A	Q
U	U	U	Q	U	A	I	N	T	U
A	I	I	A	Z	Y	Z	E	L	A
C	P	T	C	D	I	A	E	I	N
K	Q	I	G	K	U	U	U	U	T
Q	U	A	L	I	T	Y	Q	Q	I
U	A	A	N	Y	R	E	U	Q	T
I	K	U	Q	U	A	V	E	R	Y
L	E	Q	D	Q	U	A	R	R	Y
L	M	L	A	U	Q	U	I	R	K

QUA	QUACK	QUAD	QUAIL
QUAINT	QUAY	QUAKE	QUALITY
QUALM	QUANTITY	QUARRY	QUART
QUAVER	QUEEN	QUERY	QUICK
QUILL	QUILT	QUIP	QUIRK
QUIT	QUIZ		

Answer on page 77

23

The Order of Things

Put the names of the cities listed below into the grid in alphabetical order. Once you are done, read the starred column top down to find the name of the state in which all these cities are located.

Nagercoil	Tuticorin	Sivaganga
Arcot	Chennai	Madurai
Sydapet	Kanchipuram	Tond

*

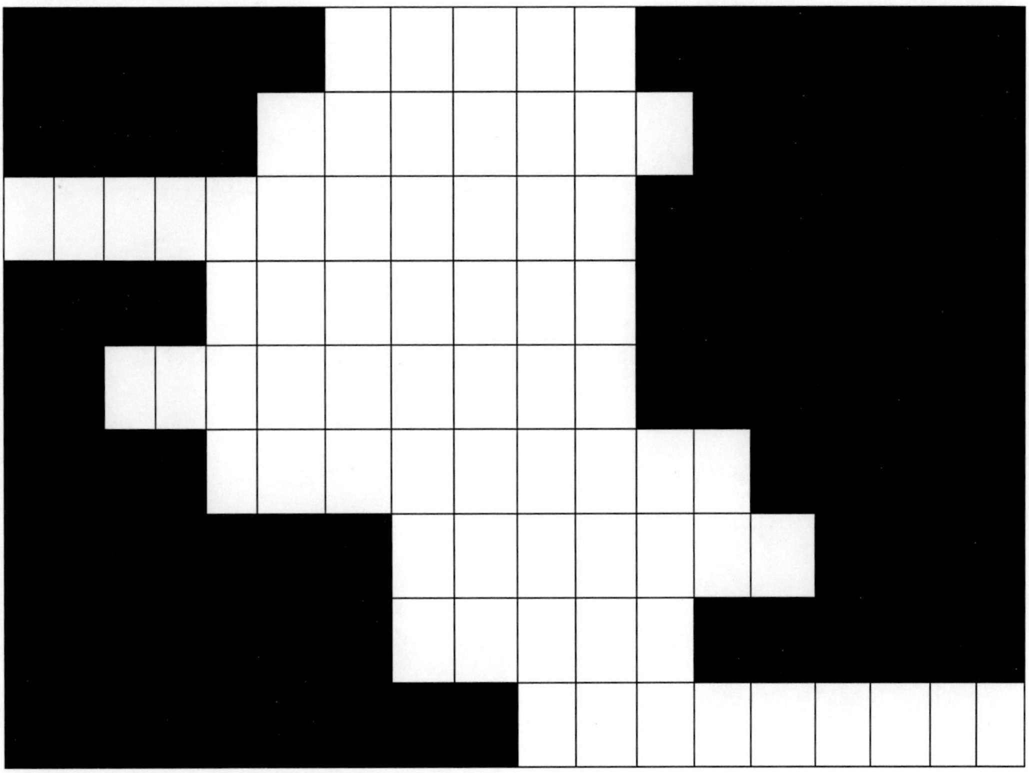

Answers on page 77

24 Pur-fect

Solve the clues to find the names of seven Indian cities that end with 'pur'.

1. The pink city ______________
2. A city famous for its oranges ______________
3. A famous bird sanctuary is located here ______________
4. The city of lakes ______________
5. The capital of chhattisgarh ______________
6. City in UP that is home to a famous engineering college ______________
7. Industrial city in Jharkhand named after Jamshedji Tata ______________

Answers on page 78

25 North-eastern Songbird

The beautiful state of Mizoram is divided into several districts. Solve the clues given below and fill in the blanks to find the names of some of the districts.

1. AIZ ___ ___ ___: a pointed tool for piercing small holes
2. ___ ___ ___ ___ ___ LEI: the air you inhale reaches one of these two
3. KOLA ___ ___ ___: the first three letters of a word for brother or sister
4. M ___ ___ IT: first person singular of the verb 'is'
5. SERCH ___ ___ ___: a synonym for 'fashionable'
6. SAI ___ ___: one syllable of the word for laughter
7. ___ ___ ___ ___ ___ ___ HAI: an informal word for 'winner'

Answers on page 78

26 On Top of the World

The letters in the names of some mountain ranges of India have been scrambled. Unscramble each using as a clue the name of a hill station (given in brackets) situated in that mountain range.

1. VALLARIA Range (Mount Abu): __________ Range
2. RAPPALJIN Range (Gulmarg): ____ ________ Range
3. RUPASTA Range (Panchmari): _________ Range
4. WRENSET HAGST (Matheran): _________ _______ Range
5. LAIP (Kodaikanal): _____ Hills
6. NETRASE GASHT (Anantagiri): _________ _______ Range
7. HARDHAULDA (Dalhousie): _____________ Range
8. HARLWAG (Dhanaulti): _________ Hills

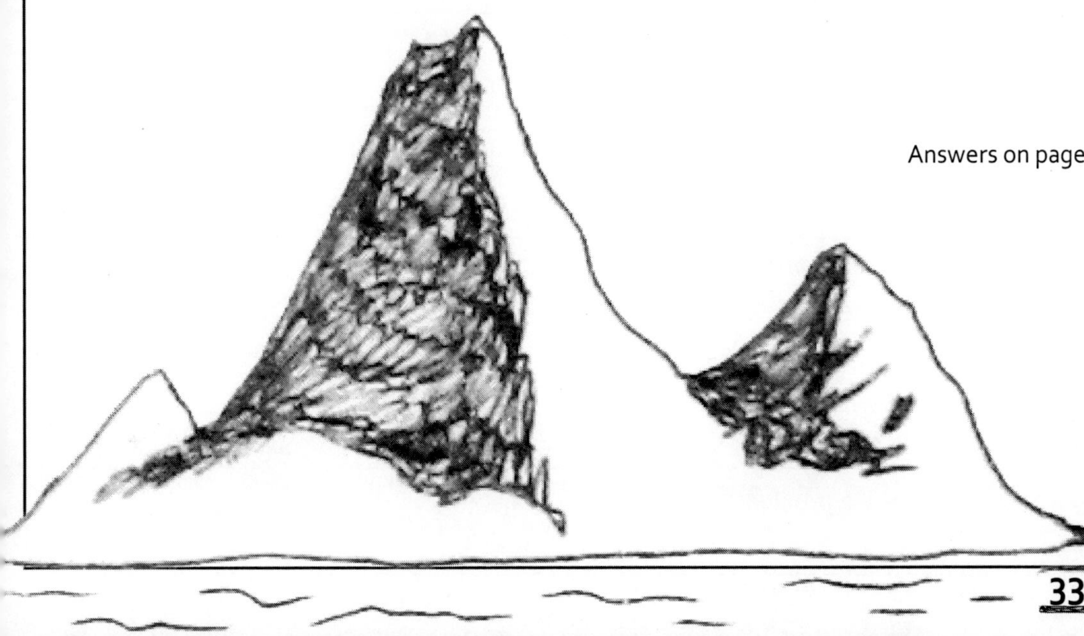

Answers on page 78

27

Add it Up

The names of some cities have been broken up into three two-letter groups (GUNTUR = GU, NT, UR) and put into three different columns (A,B and C) in a jumbled order. Put together three letter-groups, one from each column to get the name of the city that corresponds to the given clue. Strike out the two-letter groups as you go along. Write the names of the cities in the last column.

Clue	A	B	C	City
1. district in Andhra Pradesh	~~GU~~	NC	IN	GUNTUR
2. located in South Gujarat; sister city of Leicester, UK	RA	MO	RE	
3. city in Madhya Pradesh known for the Mahakal Temple	UJ	~~NT~~	RO	
4. capital of Manipur	IM	CH	IN	
5. capital of Jharkhand	RA	ZA	AL	
6. city in Haryana founded by a Kaurava warrior known for his generosity	KA	KA	OT	
7. this city in Karnataka shares its name with a palace and a sweet dish	MY	MB	RA	
8. a coastal city; called the Gateway to Kerala	CO	DO	AL	
9. capital of Mizoram	AI	JA	RA	
10. city in Jharkhand famous for its steel plant	BO	NA	HI	
11. city in Madhya Pradesh famous for the Lalbagh Palace	IN	RN	~~UR~~	
12. district in the Kumaon region of Uttarakhand	AL	SO	RK	
13. district of Himachal Pradesh	KA	JK	AI	
14. the famous Sun Temple is located in this city of Orissa	KO	NG	WL	
15. the Gateway of India is located here	MU	PH	RE	

Answers on page 78

28

Bit by Bit

Bits and pieces of the names of ten states of India and their capitals have been given below. Identify the name of each state and its capital by the letters that are given. Remember that some states and capitals have names that have two words instead of one.

1. NAT __________

   LUR __________

2. ENG __________

   KAT __________

3. RAS __________

   UMB __________

4. HAT __________

   AIP __________

5. IKK __________

   ANG __________

6. KHA __________

   RAD __________

7. RIS __________

   NES __________

8. ARY __________

   DIG __________

Answers on page 78

Arts & Culture

29

It's Time to Celebrate!

Unscramble the letters in the following quiz and fill in the blanks with the names of festivals celebrated in India.

1. The Parsi New Year: ZOVARN: _ _ _ _ _ _ _
2. The kite-flying festival of Gujarat: AYNTAARUT: _ _ _ _ _ _ _ _ _ _
3. This Kerala festival marks the homecoming of legendary King Maveli: MOAN: _ _ _ _
4. The resurrection of Christ: TEASER: _ _ _ _ _ _
5. The birthday of the founder of Sikhism: URGUBURPA:
   _ _ _ _   _ _ _ _ _
6. The day of Gautama's birth: HADBUDMANIPUR:
   _ _ _ _ _ _   _ _ _ _ _ _ _
7. This is the birthday of the Islamic prophet: MAINDALBINU:
   _ _ _ _ _-_ _-_ _ _ _
8. The day Rama defeated Ravana: SEADRUSH: _ _ _ _ _ _ _ _ _
9. The elephant-god's birthday: SHANGERUTHAITCH:
   _ _ _ _ _ _   _ _ _ _ _ _ _ _ _
10. The forty-day fast observed by Sindhis: HALICO BIASH:
   _ _ _ _ _ _   _ _ _ _ _
11. The Mizo harvest festival celebrated in December-January: PUTWALK:
   _ _ _ _   _ _ _
12. The nine days of the Goddess in Bengal: GARUDJUPA:
   _ _ _ _ _   _ _ _ _

Answers on page 79

30 Dancing to Different Tunes

In the puzzle sets below, find the first letter of each word using the clues given. Once you are done, read the first letters top down to learn the names of renowned dance gurus.

__ NOW (to be aware of)

__ MEN (said at the end of a prayer)

__ EAT (tidy, well-ordered)

__ CROBAT (performer at a circus)

__ ITCHEN (room in which food is prepared)

__ EMOVE (get rid of)

__ ND (finish)

__ OAF (unit of bread)

__ NVELOPE (cover for a letter)

__________ __________ **(Mohiniattam dancer)**

__ ULLET (fired from a gun)

__ NCH (measure of length)

__ IGHT (not left)

__ EWEL (precious stone)

__ NIFORM (what you wear to school)

__ NKLE (foot-leg connector)

__ EAT (not for vegetarians)

__ RROW (shot from a bow)

__ OUSE (where you live)

__ RTIST (painter)

__ ICE (a staple diet of Indians)

__ AM (we spread this on bread)

__________ __________ **(Kathak dancer)**

__ IND (we use this when we think)

__ NTHEM (song for a special occasion)

__ IFFICULT (not easy)

__ ELP (to aid or assist someone)

__ RK (Noah's boat)

__ EGETABLES (eat these for good health)

__ NDIGO (shade of blue)

__ ARBLE (floor stone)

__ NDERSTAND (figure out)

__ RAMA (play for the theatre)

__ ARDEN (pretty piece of land)

__ MBULANCE (to the hospital)

__ AUGH (the opposite of 'cry')

__________ __________ **(Odissi dancer)**

Answers on page 79

31 Prized Authors

Given below are names of some famous Indian authors. Use the lengths of the names to fill in the grid.

1. Premchand—Hindi (9)
2. Amrita Pritam—Punjabi (12)
3. Rabindranath Tagore—Bengali (18)
4. Vijay Tendulkar—Marathi (14)
5. Ruskin Bond—English (10)
6. Kamleshwar—Hindi (10)
7. Indira Goswami—Assamese (13)
8. Pannalal Patel—Gujarati (13)
9. Khwairakpam Chaoba—Manipuri (17)

10. Binapani Mohanty—Oriya (15)
11. Rachakonda—Telugu (10)
12. Uroob—Malayalam (5)
13. Dinanath Nadim—Kashmiri (13)
14. Arjun Deo Charan—Rajasthani (14)

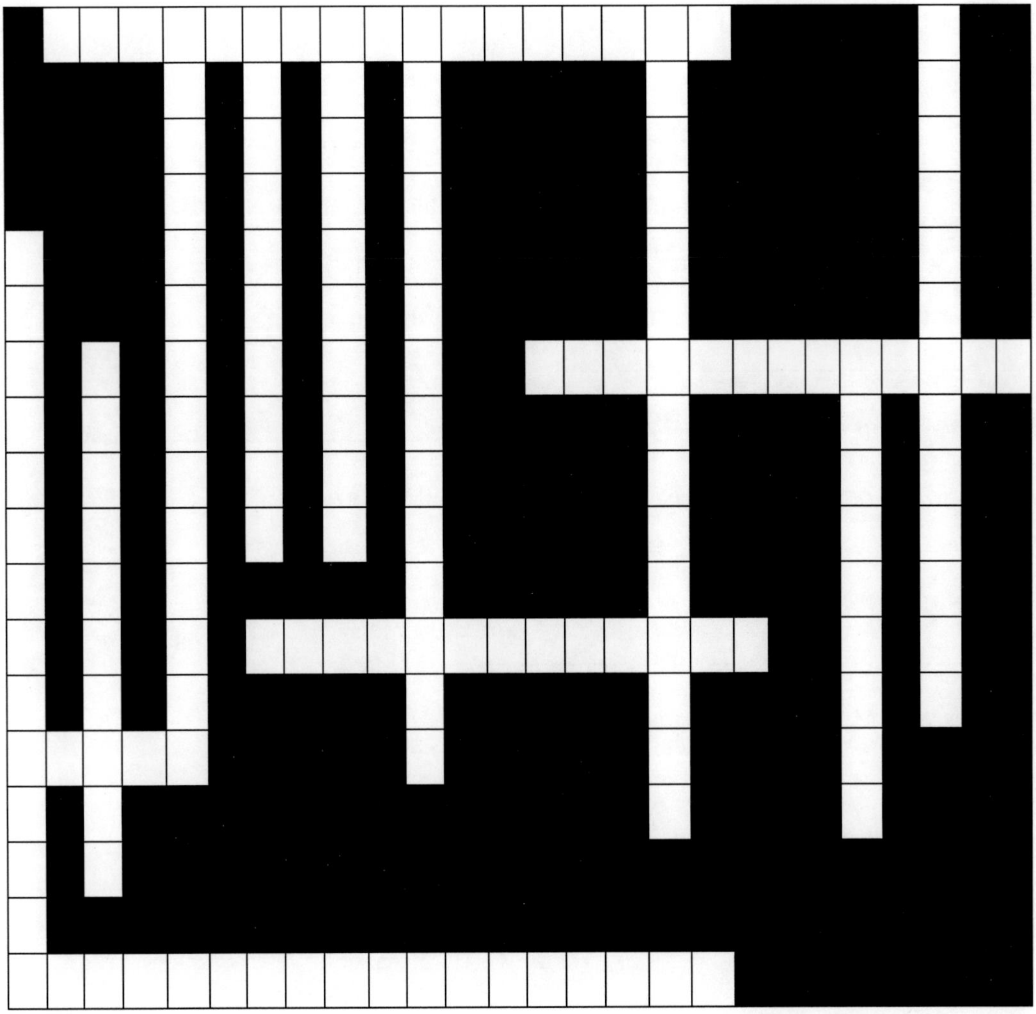

Answers on page 79

32 For You, Dear Children

Given below are the names of some Indian authors who have written in English for children. Unscramble the letters and fill in the blanks with the correct names of these famous authors.

1. *The Grasshopper's Run*—THAHARIDDS ARASM:
   _ _ _ _ _ _ _ _ _ _ _ _ _   _ _ _ _ _ _
2. *Malgudi Days*—AYANARN KR: _ _   _ _ _ _ _ _ _ _ _
3. *Haroun and the Sea of Stories*—MASALN DHURESI:
   _ _ _ _ _ _ _   _ _ _ _ _ _ _ _
4. *Beastly Tales from Here and There*—MAKVIR HEST:
   _ _ _ _ _ _ _   _ _ _ _ _
5. *The Room on the Roof*—KURINS NOBD: _ _ _ _ _ _ _   _ _ _ _ _
6. *Zain & Ana At Least A Fish*—KASUHAN VSHRKAAARI:
   _ _ _ _ _ _ _ _   _ _ _ _ _ _ _ _ _ _ _ _ _

7. *Aditi and the One-eyed Monkey*—TINSUI MOJAHINS:
   _ _ _ _ _ _ _   _ _ _ _ _ _ _ _ _ _
8. *History, Mystery, Dal and Biryani*—HADUBSAR ESN APUGT:
   _ _ _ _ _ _ _ _ _ _   _ _ _ _   _ _ _ _ _ _
9. *The Smile of Vanuvati*—INARIH MAWSILAPGO NASNARISIV:
   _ _ _ _ _ _ _   _ _ _ _ _ _ _ _ _ _ _ _   _ _ _ _ _ _ _ _ _ _ _ _
10. *Atisa and his Time Machine*—NUA RUMAK: _ _ _   _ _ _ _ _ _

Answers on page 80

33

Magic Paint

Solve the clues given in brackets and complete the names of some famous Indian painters.

1. AKBAR PA _ _ _ _ _ _ (first three letters: structure built to obstruct the flow of water; last three letters: we use our eyes to do this)
2. AMRITA SH _ _ _ IL (reverse of the first three letters of a colour found abundantly in nature)
3. ANJO _ _ _ ELA (not tell the truth) _ _ _ ON ('all ______ are created equal')
4. AR _ _ _ A CAUR (a container used for cooking)
5. JA _ _ _ (metal container) _ _ _ (reverse of the opposite of 'happy')
6. _ _ _ INI ROY (It is spread on bread at breakfast)
7. _ _ _ _ RAVI (Hindi word for 'king') V _ _ _ A (part of the body between the shoulder and the hand)
8. _ _ _ (Sita's husband and Lakshman's brother) KU _ _ _ (reverse of the first name)
9. SA _ _ _ H (reverse of the opposite of 'stand') _ _ _ RAL (reverse of the word for a container with a handle and a lip; used to hold water)
10. _ _ _ ODH (first three letters of the word for a vessel that travels underwater) _ _ _ TA (reverse of the name of a small breed of dog)

Answers on page 80

34

Epic Proportions

Solve the clues to get the names of some characters from an Indian epic and fill them in the grid horizontally. Then read down the starred column to learn the name of the epic to which these characters belong.

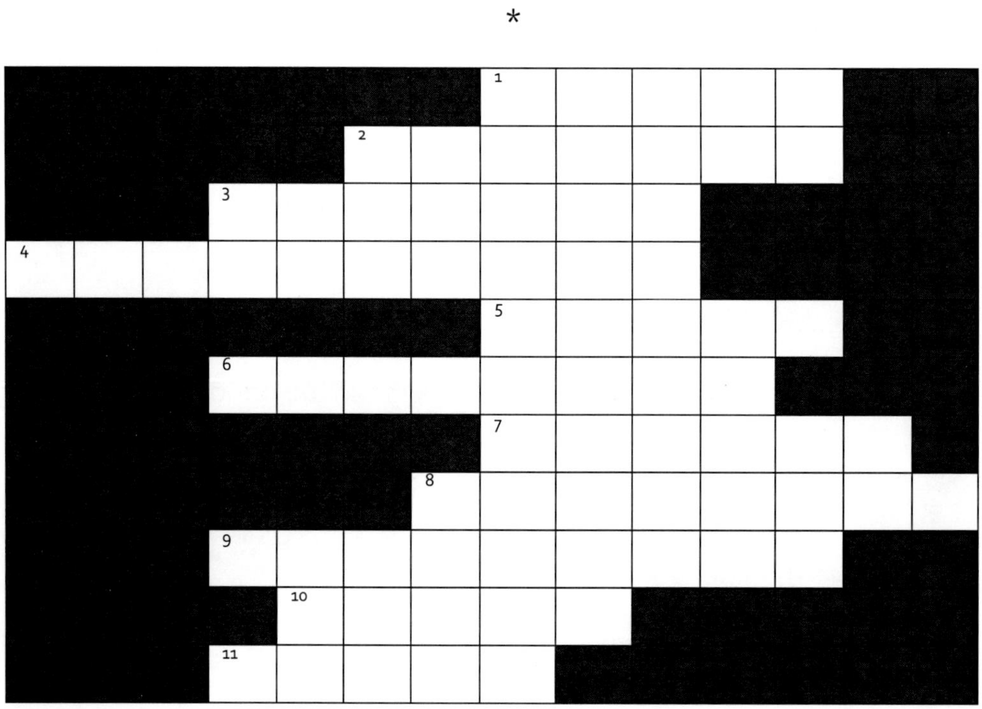

Clues:

1. Second wife of Pandu, mother of Nakul and Sahadev (5) _ _ _ _ _
2. Uncle to the kaurava brothers, he asks the pandavas to play a game of dice (7) _ _ _ _ _ _ _
3. Uncle to Dhritarashtra, he has the power to choose the time of his death (7) _ _ _ _ _ _ _

4. Dhritarashtra's eldest son (10) _ _ _ _ _ _ _ _ _ _

5. Yudhisthira's younger brother, known for his strength (5) _ _ _ _ _

6. Dhritarashtra's wife, who chooses to blindfold herself when her husband turns blind (8) _ _ _ _ _ _ _ _

7. Drona's favourite pupil, known for his archery (6) _ _ _ _ _ _

8. Wife of the pandava brothers (8) _ _ _ _ _ _ _ _

9. Duryodhana's younger brother (9) _ _ _ _ _ _ _ _ _

10. Pandu's first wife (5) _ _ _ _ _

11. The first son of Pandu and his first wife (5) _ _ _ _ _

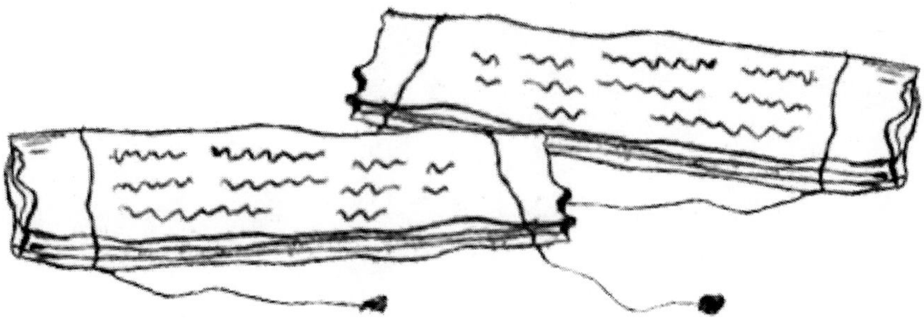

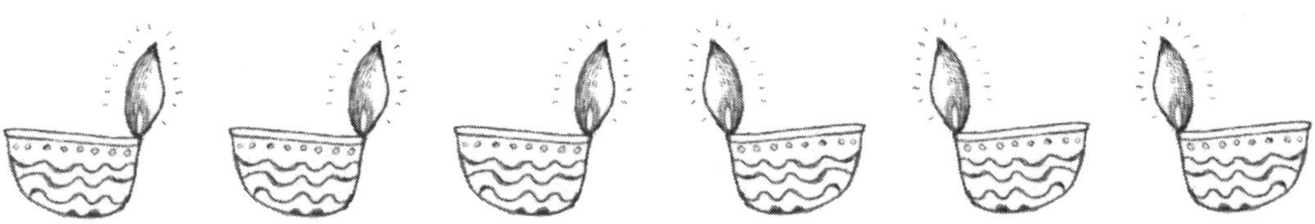

Answers on page 80

Music & Movies

35

Bollyhoo!

This Award is given annually by the Indian government for lifetime contribution to Indian cinema. Solve the clues given below to find the names of Bollywood personalities and fill them in horizontally. The figures in brackets indicate the number of letters in the name. Then read down the starred column to find the name of the Award.

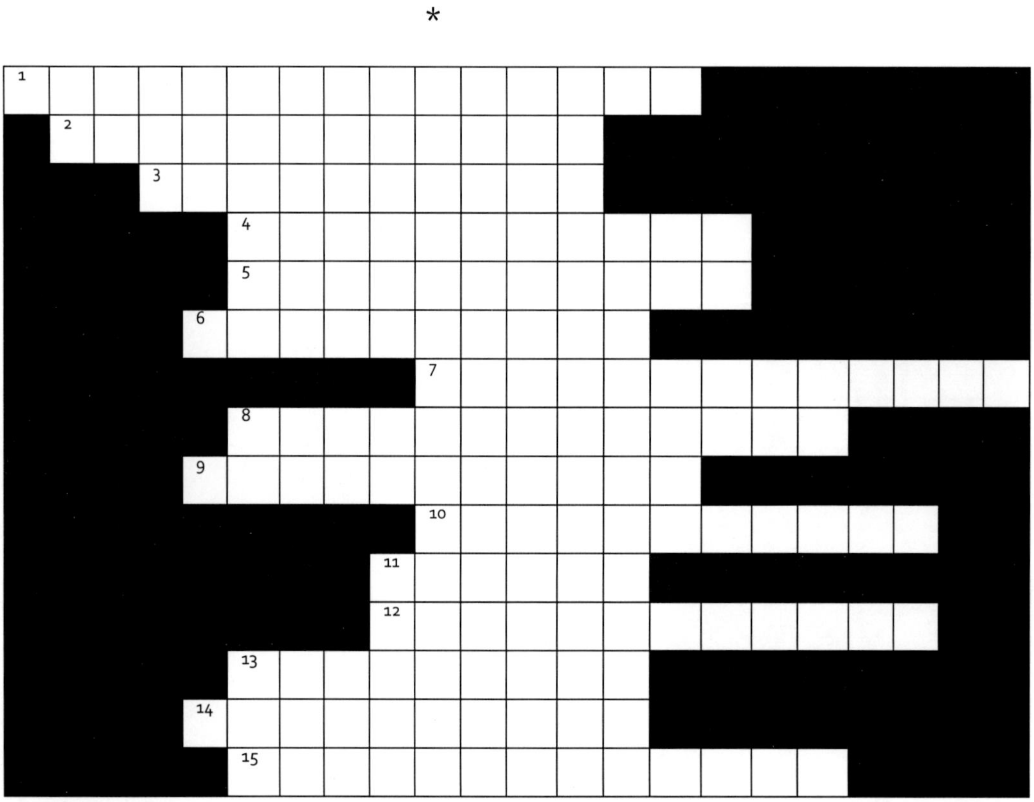

1. Before joining films, she was a state-level badminton player and a model. (15)

2. She won the Miss World competition and is now married to the son of an Indian superstar. (12)

3. Munnabhai's name in real life (10)
4. The son of a cricketer and a film actress; his sister is also a well-known actress. (11)
5. Initially a model, she is now an actress known for her high level of fitness.(11)
6. The invisible man of Mr. India becomes quizmaster for *Slumdog Millionaire*. (10)
7. His dance moves are the envy of everyone. (13)
8. She ushered in 'size zero'. (13)
9. He worked in advertising before joining films; motorbikes are his passion. (11)
10. The 'bubbly' actress with deep dimples (11)
11. The name of the movie featuring Gabbar Singh. (6)
12. An actor in the same movie, he once played nine roles in a different film. (12)
13. He was in Bengali theatre and films, and was known for his comic roles in Hindi movies with actors such as Amol Palekar, Dharmendra and Sharmila Tagore. (9)
14. He played the role of Prince Salim in Mughal-e-Azam. (10)
15. The star of Gurudutt's classic movies (13)

Answers on page 81

36 Instrumental

Given below are the names of some Indian musical instruments, with their letters scrambled. Rearrange the letters to find the name of each instrument.

1. I STAR __________
2. ROADS __________
3. AN EVE __________
4. ROAST ON __________
5. A TREK A __________
6. A GRAINS __________
7. U BRAINS __________
8. JAM RAIN __________
9. LA BAT __________
10. A DRUM A __________
11. DRAG MAIN M __________
12. TAJ LANGAR __________
13. HORN GOUG __________
14. JAVA KHAP __________

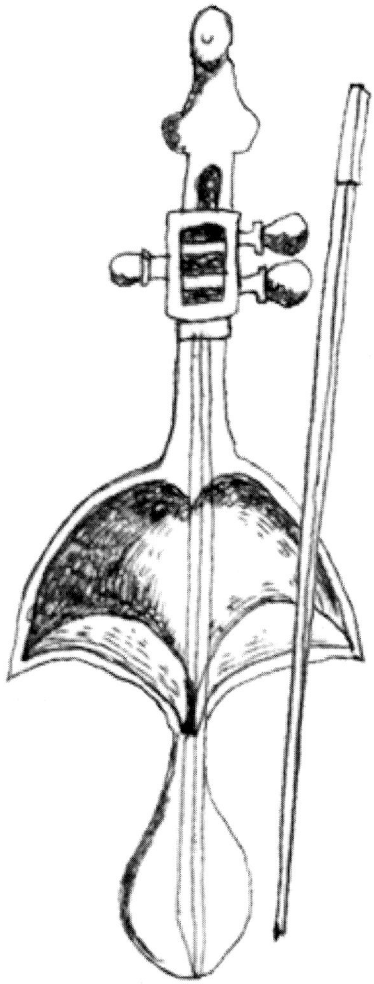

Anwers on page 81

37 And the Oscar Goes To . . .

Identify the Oscar-winning Indian director by inserting the names of his movies into the grid and then reading down the starred column. The figures in the brackets indicate the number of letters in the movie title.

Ashani Sanket (12) Bala (4) Jalsaghar (9)

Jana Aranya (10) Kapurush (8) Nayak (5)

Pather Panchali (14) Sadgati (7) The Inner Eye (11)

The World of Apu (13) Two (3)

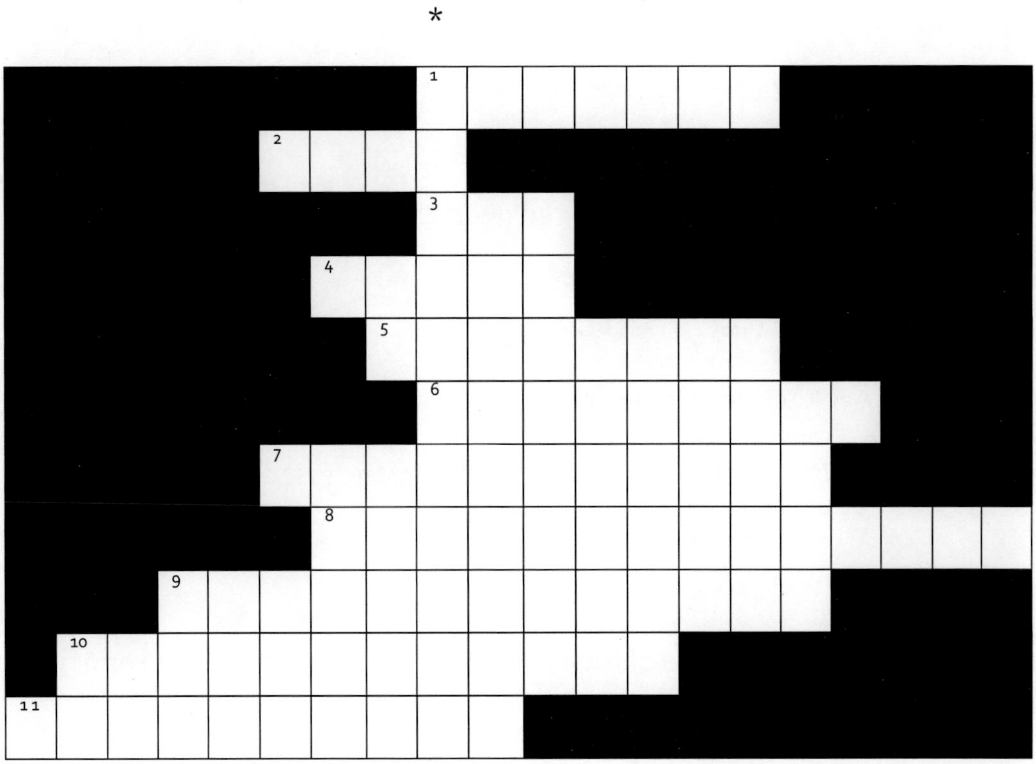

Answers on page 82

38

Strike a Tune

In the four puzzle sets below, the first three letters of the incomplete words are the same. Solve the clues to find the three letters, and then use the three letters to get the name of a raga.

__ __ __ N G R A (Punjabi folk dance)

__ __ __ R A T P U R (sanctuary for migratory birds in Rajasthan)

__ __ __ I R A V I (the raga that is played during the early part of the evening)

__ __ __ K (little or no light)

__ __ __ T S (an indoor game with a circular numbered board at which players throw pointed missiles)

__ __ __ B A R I (the raga that is played deep into the night)

__ __ __ A H A R I (a desert in southern Africa)

__ __ __ I D A S A (ancient Indian playwright known for his play *Shakuntala*)

__ __ __ Y A N I (the raga that is performed during the first quarter of the night)

__ __ __ M E R (tool used to drive nails in)

__ __ __ M O C K (bed made of rope and tied to trees or poles at the ends)

__ __ __ S A D H W A N I (the raga that is performed during the second quarter of the night)

Answers on page 82

All Creatures Great and Small

39

Jungle Adventure

Given below are names of famous Indian wild animals. Fill in the grid using the lengths of the words.

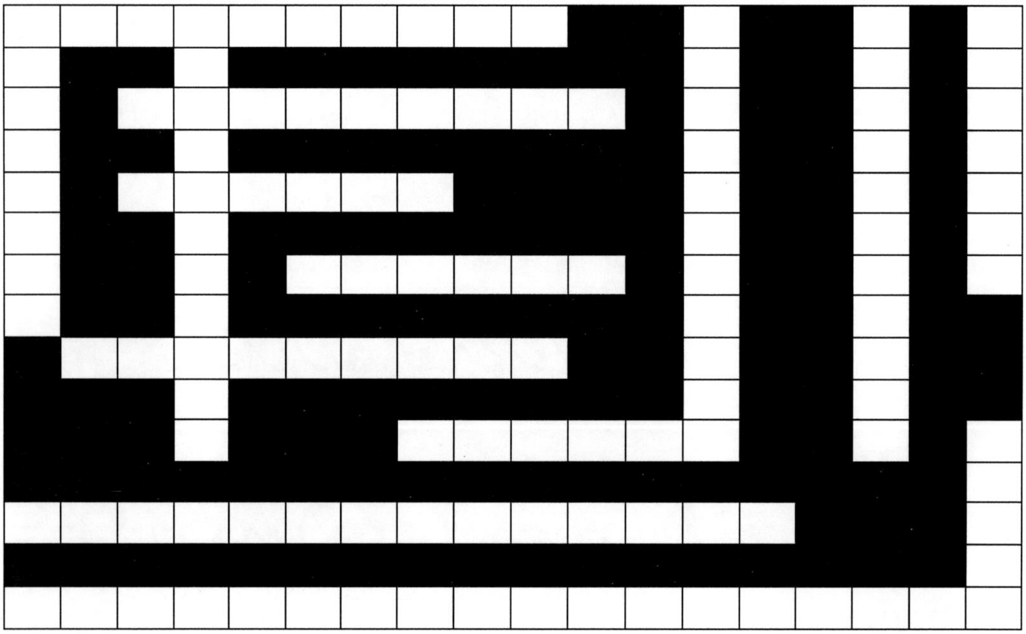

ACROSS

Rhinoceros (10)

Blackbuck (9)

Nilgai (6)

Himalayan black bear (18)

Blue sheep (9)

Flying squirrel (14)

Python 6)

Sambar (6)

DOWN

Nilgiri tahr (11)

Snow leopard (11)

Gharial (7)

Red panda (8)

Tiger (5)

Indian bison (11)

Answers on page 83

40 Spot the Tiger

Name fifteen famous tiger reserves in India by solving the clues given.

1. This National Park lies along the Mysore-Ooty highway.
   _ _ _ _ _ _ _ _ National Park

2. Located in district Lakhimpur, Uttar Pradesh, this national park lies along the Indo-Nepal border. _ _ _ _ _ _ National Park

3. This forest in Orissa is also famous for its waterfalls.
   _ _ _ _ _ _ _ _ National Park

4. This Park is also famous for the elusive snow leopard and the clouded leopard. _ _ _ _ _ _ _ _ National Park

5. It is located in the Mandla district of Madhya Pradesh, in a valley shaped like a horseshoe. _ _ _ _ _ National Park

6. Located in Madhya Pradesh, the famous white tigers of Rewa were discovered here. _ _ _ _ _ _ _ _ _ _ _ National Park

7. This dense forest is located in the foothills of the Himalayas and named in honour of the late hunter-naturalist turned author.
   _ _ _ _ _ _ _ National Park

8. It is located in Rajasthan, near Sawai Madhopur.
   _ _ _ _ _ _ _ _ _ _ _ National Park

9. This forest lies in the largest estuarine delta in the world.
   _ _ _ _ _ _ _ _ _ _ National Park

10. This is the place to go if you want to see the one-horned rhino.
   _ _ _ _ _ _ _ _ _ National Park

11. This Park is located in Nilgiri district, Tamil Nadu, near Coimbatore. _ _ _ _ _ _ _ _ _ _ National Park

12. This is part of the Aravalli range, in the Alwar district of Rajasthan. _ _ _ _ _ _ _ _ National Park

13. This is a protected area in the East Kameng district of Arunachal Pradesh. _ _ _ _ _ _ _ Tiger Reserve

14. This is located partly in Madhya Pradesh and partly in Maharashtra. _ _ _ _ _ _ Tiger Reserve

15. This is the largest wildlife sanctuary in Mizoram. _ _ _ _ _ _ Tiger Reserve

Answers on page 83

Food for Thought

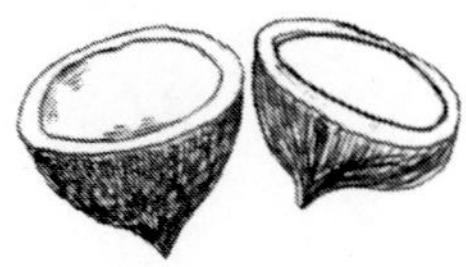

On the Menu

The letters of the names of popular dishes and the states they come from have been mixed together. However, the letters have been placed in the correct order. Separate the letters and write the name of each state and dish in the blanks.

1. R O J A M G A M U N A N J D K A S O H M S I H R
   State: __________ Dish: __________
2. S W A E N S T D E B E S N G H A L
   State: __________ Dish: __________
3. R D A A L B J A A T S I T C H H U A R M N A
   State: __________ Dish: __________
4. P S A R U S N O N K J A S A A A B G
   State: __________ Dish: __________
5. M A S O S R J A H M O L
   State: __________ Dish: __________
6. S G H U R J I A K H R A A N T D
   State: __________ Dish: __________
7. P O M O A R H A A N R A P S O H L T I R A
   State: __________ Dish: __________
8. B A N I S I D H B E R L A E H P R U L A I D A E S N N H A
   State: __________ Dish: __________
9. K N A E L G A H L A N E D
   State: __________ Dish: __________
10. N A U R T G T A R I S P I R A K D O F E S T H A
    State: __________ Dish: __________

Answers on page 84

42

The Spice of Life

The names of fifteen spices are mixed up in this long sequence of letters. The first fifteen letters are the first letters of each of the spices. The letters of the spices are in the correct order. Identify the spices using the clues given.

N F G S C C P C C M C C P F G

U A F I H O O E A E T I N N N

L O V E E I U U A R R M N N G

F R P L M S R I P N L E E E O

A I O A U I C G L R N M P E L

I N T A M N P G R O N R R D D

E Y E E R K

1. This tree and its seed have the same name. The seed has a reddish lacy covering, which is the spice mace. __ __ __ __ __ __

2. Its green seeds are a popular mouth freshener. __ __ __ __ __ __

3. It grows as a root and is found in various cuisines of India. It has a fiery taste, is added to tea in winter, and is known to aid digestion. __ __ __ __ __ __

4. This is the world's most expensive spice by weight. It is grown in Kashmir and is used as a colouring and seasoning agent. __ __ __ __ __ __ __

5. This spice is obtained from the inner barks of trees, and is used in both sweet and savoury foods. __ __ __ __ __ __ __ __

6. It is the flower bud of a tree, and is used to treat toothache. __ __ __ __ __

7. It is hot to taste, and is available in three colours—black, white, green.
_ _ _ _ _ _

8. It adds a fiery taste to a dish, and is available as whole fresh fruit, whole dried fruit, and in powdered form. _ _ _ _ _ _

9. Its seeds are yellow-brown in colour and splutter in hot oil. _ _ _ _ _

10. The seeds of this spice are round, and yellowish-white to black in colour. The name of the spice is also the name of a colour. _ _ _ _ _ _ _

11. Its seeds are small, egg-shaped and grayish. It is popular as a digestive aid, and is extensively used to make parathas. _ _ _ _ _

12. This spice consists of dried seeds in whole or powdered form. The seeds thicken dishes to which they are added, and are boiled in water to make a home-based cure for colds. The leaves and dried seeds are used in cooking. _ _ _ _ _ _ _ _ _

13. It is a tiny oilseed used in baked goods, curries and desserts. It is also a popular component of birdseed. _ _ _ _ _

14. The leaves of this plant are eaten. Fresh or dried leaves are used to flavour certain dishes. The seeds are popular as well.
_ _ _ _ _ _ _ _ _

15. It belongs to the onion family and has a pungent flavour. _ _ _ _ _ _

Answers on page 84

43

Vegetable Market

Place a letter-pair from the box below in each of the spaces provided to end the name of a place and begin the name of a vegetable. Strike off each letter-pair as you use it.

KA	MU	LI	AR	GA	RA	SH	LE	AS	ON	YA	LA

1. ABOH/___/TICHOKE
2. AYODH/___/M
3. DARBHAN/___/RLIC
4. QUIL/___/ION
5. BHILWA/___/DISH
6. DHOL/___/LE
7. SHIM/___/DY’S FINGER
8. DEW/___/PARAGUS
9. JAM/___/SHROOM
10. MADANAPAL/___/EK
11. RISHIKE/___/ALLOT
12. HUB/___/MA BEAN

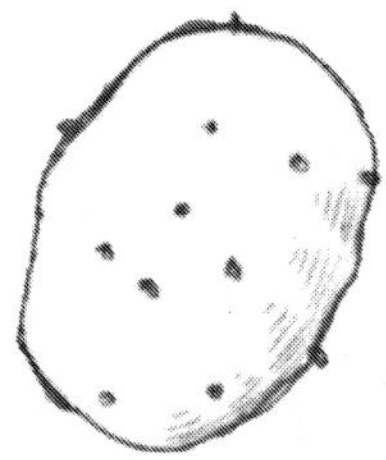

Answers on page 84

44

Crop Matters

The words given below the grid have something in common. Strike them out horizontally, vertically, and diagonally in the grid. Arrange the leftover letters in order to find out what they have in common.

R	T	C	T	U	N	O	C	O	C
E	U	A	E	J	S	O	A	O	I
G	N	B	A	U	T	E	F	G	R
N	A	H	B	T	T	F	L	I	E
I	C	C	O	E	E	R	O	D	M
G	E	N	O	E	R	P	O	N	R
R	R	C	A	S	H	E	W	I	U
A	A	S	O	C	C	A	B	O	T
M	E	N	A	C	R	A	G	U	S
S	E	S	A	M	E	Z	I	A	M

ARECA NUT CASHEW COFFEE COCONUT

COTTON GINGER GRAM INDIGO

JUTE MAIZE RUBBER SESAME

SUGARCANE TEA TOBACCO TURMERIC

WOOL

Answers on page 85

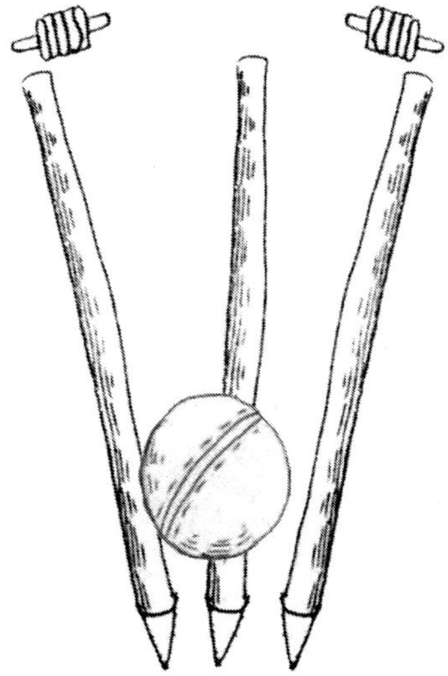

All Things Indian

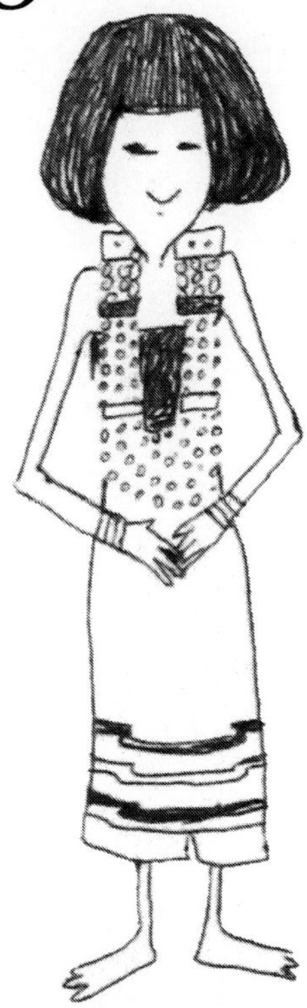

45 National Identity

Solve the clues given below and fill in the blanks. Once you have filled in all the answers, rearrange the letters in the boxes to find the theme of the puzzle.

1. National bird: _ _ ☐ _ _ _ _

2. National fruit: ☐☐☐ _ ☐

3. National flower: ☐☐ _ _ ☐

4. National tree: ☐ _ _ _ _ _

5. National anthem: _ _ ☐ _   _ _ _ _   _ _ _ _

6. National game: _ _ _ _ _ ☐

7. National animal: ☐☐ _ _ _

Theme of the puzzle: _ _ _ _ _ _ _ L   _ _ _ _ _ _ S

Answers on page 85

46 Mind Your Language

Rearrange the letters of the names of some Indian languages in each of the two groups and fill in the blanks and the boxes. Read the letters in the boxes top down and you will have the names of two ancient Indian scripts.

ABIGLEN: ☐ _ _ _ _ _ _

RYOIA: _ ☐ _ _ _

LITMA: _ ☐ _ _ _

HISDIN: _ _ _ _ ☐ _

THAMIAR: ☐ _ _ _ _ _ ☐

Script: ____________________

RAJGUITA: ☐ _ _ _ _ _ _ _

DUUR : _ ☐ _ _

DANKANA: _ ☐ _ ☐ _ _ _

GULTUE: ☐ _ _ _ _ _

SIAKH: _ ☐ _ _ _

INKONKA: _ _ _ _ ☐ _ _

Script: ____________________

Answers on page 85

47

Tribal Themes

In each of the five puzzle sets below, the first three letters of the words are the same. Solve the clues and fill in the three letters. The last word in each set will be the name of an Indian tribe.

___ ___ ___ D (deserts are covered with this)

___ ___ ___ S K R I T (an ancient Indian language)

___ ___ ___ T H A L S (a tribe from eastern India)

___ ___ ___ G L E S (jewellery worn around the wrist)

___ ___ ___ A N A (you can slip on the peel of this fruit and fall)

___ ___ ___ J A R A (a nomadic tribe from western India)

___ ___ ___ D O L A (boats used for transportation in Venice, Italy)

___ ___ ___ G (round metal disc that makes a loud sound on being struck)

___ ___ ___ D S (the largest tribe in South Asia)

___ ___ ___ C H (chew noisily)

___ ___ ___ D A N E (dull)

___ ___ ___ D A (this tribe is found mainly in Jharkhand)

___ ___ ___ F (a cook in a restaurant)

___ ___ ___ A P (not expensive)

___ ___ ___ N C H U (a tribe from Andhra Pradesh)

Answers on page 86

48 Mining for Treasure

The names of some minerals found in India are given in a jumbled form below. Each jumble is accompanied by a clue. Solve the clues, unscramble the letters, and write the names of the minerals in the blanks alongside.

MINIMULUA (foil is made of this metal) __________

BLOCTA (it is a also a shade of the colour blue) __________

PORPEC (good quality electrical wires are made of this) __________

LOCA (a common source of electricity) __________

MADDINO (a sparkling stone, the hardest substance known) __________

DOGL (a precious metal) __________

PITEGHRA (pencil lead is made of this) __________

ROONER (used to make steel) ____ ____

MUNIARU (a radioactive metal) __________

IZCN (combined with copper to make brass) __________

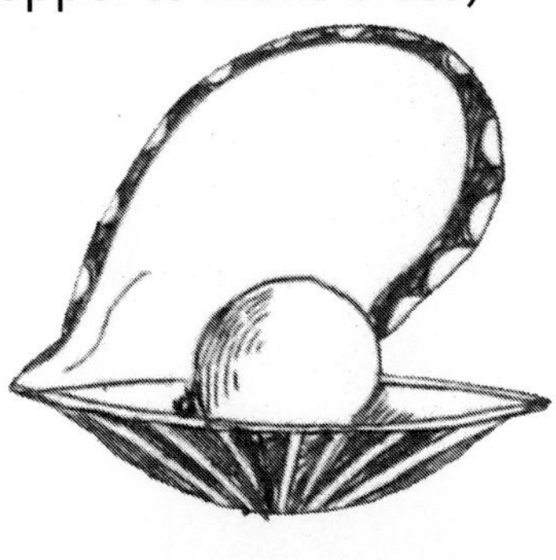

Answers on page 86

Sparkling Stones

Strike off the names of precious and semi-precious stones in the grid below to find the name of a famous mine in India and what is mined there.

T	O	U	R	M	A	L	I	N	E	G	L
N	B	Q	T	O	P	A	Z	N	T	A	Y
A	S	U	S	A	R	D	I	U	I	R	R
I	I	A	K	O	L	R	R	O	T	N	E
L	D	R	A	R	T	Q	G	N	A	E	B
E	I	T	O	I	U	L	D	Y	M	T	D
N	A	Z	C	O	R	A	L	X	E	L	I
R	N	L	I	R	E	B	M	A	A	E	A
A	M	S	R	J	A	D	E	R	H	N	M
C	E	I	C	A	T	S	E	Y	E	I	O
L	O	L	I	T	E	M	N	E	S	P	N
R	U	B	Y	R	E	P	S	A	J	S	D

Amber
Beryl
Carnelian
Cat's eye
Citrine
Coral
Diamond
Emerald
Garnet
Haematite
Lolite
Jade
Jasper
Obsidian
Onyx
Pearl
Quartz
Ruby
Sard
Spinel
Topaz
Tourmaline
Turquoise

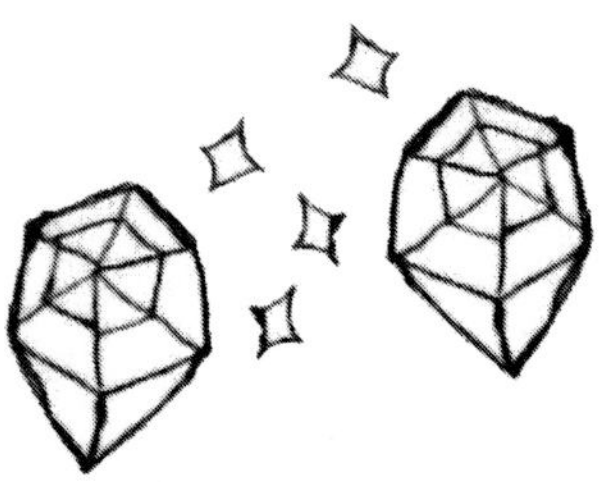

Answers on page 86

50

Win-win Situation

The names of 15 trophies have been broken up into three letter-groups. Match a letter-group in column A with groups in columns B and C to complete the name of a trophy for the sport mentioned alongside as a clue. Write the names of the cups on the blanks, and strike off each letter-group as you use it.

Example: DU, RA, ND for Durand.

	A	**B**	**C**	**City**	**Sport**
1.	~~*DU*~~	IJ	AR	*DURAND*	football
2.	CH	AR	AL	__________	badminton
3.	RA	LK	WAN	__________	cricket
4.	NA	BR	HA	__________	badminton
5.	RO	~~*RA*~~	OSH	__________	football
6.	DU	IGH	NG	__________	cricket
7.	HO	ODH	RS	__________	bridge
8.	VI	NT	TON	__________	football
9.	BU	RM	~~*ND*~~	__________	weight-lifting
10.	DE	VE	WAL	__________	cricket

11.	SA	AD	EP	__________	football
12.	GU	TT	OTO	__________	hockey
13.	AG	LE	IT	__________	badminton
14.	BE	RD	AR	__________	hockey
15.	SU	RA	EET	__________	football

Answers on page 86

Answers

Historic India

1. Father of Our Nation

1. Porbandar
2. Rajkot
3. Bhavnagar
4. London
5. Bombay
6. Natal
7. Ahmedabad
8. Amritsar
9. Bombay
10. Chauri Chaura
11. Dandi
12. Delhi

2. India Reformed

1. Acharya Vinoba Bhave
2. Baba Amte
3. Dr. B. R. Ambedkar
4. Ishwar Chandra Vidyasagar
5. Shri Ramakrishna Paramahansa
6. Jyotiba Phule
7. Mother Teresa
8. Annie Besant
9. Swami Dayanand Saraswati
10. Raja Ram Mohan Roy

3. The Presidential Seal

R Venkataraman – was a delegate to the UN General Assembly

Dr Rajendra Prasad – India's first President

Giani Zail Singh – served as Chief Minister of Punjab

Dr Fakhruddin Ali Ahmed – died while in office

Dr Sarvapalli Radhakrishnan – Teachers' Day is celebrated on his birthday

Dr APJ Abdul Kalam – Missile Man of India

Pratibha Devisingh Patil – India's first woman President

Dr VV Giri – was awarded the Bharat Ratna

KR Narayanan – served as India's Ambassador to the US

Dr Zakir Hussain – established Jamia Millia Islamia

Neelam Sanjiva Reddy – first Chief Minister of Andhra Pradesh

Shankar Dayal Sharma – swore in three Prime Ministers in one year

4. Words of Wisdom

Water, Blue, Church, Dog, Sign, Maybe

'Be the change you wish to see in the world.' – Mahatma Gandhi

5. Ancient Times

1. Pulses 2. Amulet 3. Immune 4. Tablet 5. Height
6. Annual 7. Neighs

Ancient cities: Paithan, Lumbini

6. Hold the Fort

Kokila / Lal Qila

Neelam / Amber

Manju / Junagadh

Salome / Mehrangarh

Enoch / Chittorgarh

Shailaja / Jaisalmer

Pappu / Purana Qila

Sameera / Ranthambore

Margo/ Golconda

Mustafa / Fatehpur Sikri

Suresh / Shaniwar Wada

Ramu / Murud Janjira

7. Heritage Sites

1-g, 2-d, 3-j, 4-b, 5-h, 6-a, 7-i, 8-m, 9-n, 10-k, 11-f, 12-c, 13-e, 14-l

8. Words of Wisdom 2

Tabla, Duckling, Grey, Show, Movie

'The world is the great gymnasium where we come to make ourselves strong.' – Swami Vivekananda

Around the Country in 20 Puzzles

9. Matters of State

							*							
						A	C	H	H	O	T	A		
						C	H	I	T	R	A	K	O	T
		D	H	O	N	D	H	A	T	A	R	A	I	
D	O	N	G	A	R	G	A	O	N					
					H	A	T	T	I	G	A	M		
				K	A	N	T	E	L	I				
			K	A	R	S	I							
					K	U	S	U	M	K	A	S	A	
	M	A	L	K	A	N	G	I	R	I				
				P	A	L	A	U	D					
				S	A	T	R	E	N	G	A			
			S	I	N	G	H	O	R	A				

10. Call a City by a New Name

Quilon – Kollam
Madras – Chennai
Trivandrum – Thiruvananthapuram
Calicut – Kozhikode
Calcutta – Kolkata
Coorg – Kodagu
Benares – Varanasi
Bombay – Mumbai
Baroda – Vadodara
Cochin – Kochi
Trichur – Thrissoor

11. District-wise

S T S A B A	I B O A D R	S S A A S A	B C O A F A
K O P P A L	M A N D Y A	H A S S A N	Y A D G I R
Y N Y E T E	P N E D E G	E P K H T T	E D E E R K

12. Mountains to Climb

Drape	Waist
Bored	Lurid
Amuse	Slink
Piper	Wager
Aster	Talon
Stake	Coins
Bushy	Manic

13. A River is the Sum of its Parts

H	O	N	N	U	H	O	L	E	T
E	I	K	S	**K**	**A**	**V**	**E**	I	A
M	N	A	H	**R**	**I**	**K**	R	**R**	N
A	A	P	I	**I**	**S**	T	I	**H**	A
V	V	I	M	**N**	H	N	**A**	**R**	M
A	A	L	S	A	I	**A**	**J**	**A**	H
T	H	A	H	B	**S**	**A**	**G**	**A**	S
I	B	L	A	Y	Y	O	N	**R**	K
A	R	K	A	V	A	T	H	Y	A

Name of the river: Kaveri

Name of dam across the river: Krishna Raja Sagar

14. Fruity Places

1. Mangalore (Mango)
2. Banswara (Banana)
3. Jamnagar (Jamun)
4. Cochin (Coconut)
5. Cherapunji (Cherry)
6. Melur (Melon)
7. Durgapur (Durian)
8. Cranganore (Cranberry)

15. City Slickers

1. Kurukshetra
2. Madurai
3. Varanasi
4. Bhopal
5. Coimbatore
6. Calicut
7. Dharamsala
8. Agartala
9. Dimapur
10. Kohima

16. Going Bad

1. Hyderabad
2. Allahabad
3. Ahmedabad
4. Aurangabad
5. Firozabad

17. On the Road

1. Durgapur
2. Aurangabad
3. Asansol
4. Varanasi
5. Dhanbad
6. Amritsar
7. Aligarh
8. Ludhiana
9. Jalandhar
10. Kolkata

Answer: Grand Trunk Road

18. Mountain Meadows

Knife	Lamb	Good
Abode	Umbrella	Ugly
Night	Desert	Listen
Green	Upper	Market
Water	Raven	Alien
Again	Menu	River
Table	Army	Guest
Apple	Right	
Mother	Garage	
Kangwatan	**Ludurmarg**	**Gulmarg**

19. Read Between the Letters

1. Nap
2. Jaw
3. Rust
4. Tan
5. Panda
6. Risk
7. Low
8. Tank
9. Angle
10. Bike
11. Combat
12. Ark
13. Ring
14. Gum

20. *Changing Districts*

PURI—PURE—SURE—SORE—SOLE—SOLD

GAYA—GALA—GALE—BALE—BOLE—BOLT

PUNE—PANE—PANS—CANS—CARS—JARS

BEED—BEND—LEND—LEAD—LOAD—LOAN

TONK—TANK—DANK—DARK—DARE—PARE

JIND—JINX—MINX—MINE—MANE—MATE

21. *Changing Rivers*

RAVI—RAVE—ROVE—LOVE—LOSE—LOST

MAHI—MAGI—RAGI—RAGS—RUGS—TUGS

BEAS—BEAD—READ—ROAD—TOAD—TOLD

TAPI—TAPS—TOPS—TOTS—LOTS—LETS

BORI—BORN—BARN—BARK—BASK—TASK

SAGI—SAGE—SALE—HALE—HOLE—HOLD

22. *Q Up*

Qazigund

23. *The Order of Things*

										*							
						A	R	C	O	T							
					C	H	E	N	N	A	I						
K	A	N	C	H	I	P	U	R	A	M							
				M	A	D	U	R	A	I							
		N	A	G	E	R	C	O	I	L							
				S	I	V	A	G	A	N	G	A					
							S	Y	D	A	P	E	T				
							T	O	N	D	I						
									T	U	T	I	C	O	R	I	N

24. Pur-fect

1. Jaipur
2. Nagpur
3. Bharatpur
4. Udaipur
5. Raipur
6. Kanpur
7. Jamshedpur

25. North-eastern Songbird

1. Aizawl
2. Lunglei
3. Kolasib
4. Mamit
5. Serchhip
6. Saiha
7. Champhai

26. On Top of the World

1. Aravalli Range
2. Pir Panjal Range
3. Satpura Range
4. Western Ghats Range
5. Pali Hills
6. Eastern Ghats
7. Dhauladhar Range
8. Garhwal Hills

27. Add it Up

1. Guntur
2. Rajkot
3. Ujjain
4. Imphal
5. Ranchi
6. Karnal
7. Mysore
8. Cochin
9. Aizawl
10. Bokaro
11. Indore
12. Almora
13. Kangra
14. Konark
15. Mumbai

28. Bit by Bit

1. Karnataka – Bengaluru
2. West Bengal – Kolkata
3. Maharashtra – Mumbai
4. Chhatisgarh – Raipur
5. Sikkim – Gangtok
6. Uttarakhand – Dehradun
7. Orissa – Bhubaneshwar
8. Haryana – Chandigarh

Arts & Culture

29. It's Time to Celebrate!

1. Navroz
2. Uttarayan
3. Onam
4. Easter
5. Guru Purab
6. Buddha Purnima
7. Milad-un-Nabi
8. Dussehra
9. Ganesh Chaturthi
10. Chailo Sahib
11. Pawl Kut
12. Durga Puja

30. Dancing to Different Tunes

Kanak Rele – Mohiniattam dancer

Birju Maharaj – Kathak dancer

Madhavi Mudgal – Odissi dancer

31. Prized Authors

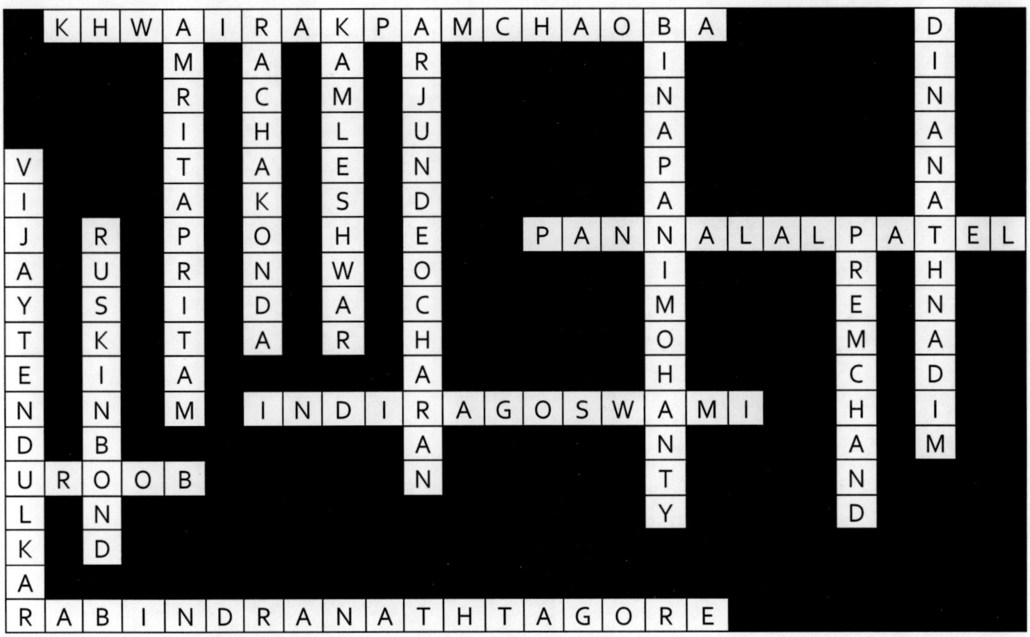

32. For You, Dear Children

1. Siddhartha Sarma
2. R.K. Narayan
3. Salman Rushdie
4. Vikram Seth
5. Ruskin Bond
6. Anushka Ravishankar
7. Suniti Namjoshi
8. Subhadra Sen Gupta
9. Harini Gopalswami Srinivasan
10. Anu Kumar

33. Magic Paint

1. Akbar Padamsee
2. Amrita Shergill
3. Anjolie Ela Menon
4. Arpana Caur
5. Jatin Das
6. Jamini Roy
7. Raja Ravi Varma
8. Ram Kumar
9. Satish Gujral
10. Subodh Gupta

34. Epic Proportions *

							M	A	D	R	I		
					S	H	A	K	U	N	I		
			B	H	I	S	H	M	A				
D	U	R	Y	O	D	H	A	N	A				
							B	H	I	M	A		
			G	A	N	D	H	A	R	I			
							A	R	J	U	N	A	
						D	R	A	U	P	A	D	I
			D	U	S	H	A	S	A	N	A		
				K	U	N	T	I					
			K	A	R	N	A						

Music & Movies

35. Bollyhoo!

									*												
D	E	E	P	I	K	A	P	A	D	U	K	O	N	E							
	A	I	S	H	W	A	R	Y	A	R	A	I									
			S	A	N	J	A	Y	D	U	T	T									
					S	A	I	F	A	L	I	K	H	A	N						
					B	I	P	A	S	H	A	B	A	S	U						
				A	N	I	L	K	A	P	O	O	R								
									H	R	I	T	H	I	K	R	O	S	H	A	N
					K	A	R	E	E	N	A	K	A	P	O	O	R				
				J	O	H	N	A	B	R	A	H	A	M							
									P	R	E	I	T	Y	Z	I	N	T	A		
								S	H	O	L	A	Y								
								S	A	N	J	E	E	V	K	U	M	A	R		
					U	T	P	A	L	D	U	T	T								
				D	I	L	I	P	K	U	M	A	R								
					W	A	H	E	E	D	A	R	E	H	M	A	N				

36. Instrumental

1. Sitar
2. Sarod
3. Veena
4. Santoor
5. Ektara
6. Sarangi
7. Bansuri
8. Manjira
9. Tabla
10. Damaru
11. Mridangam
12. Jaltarang
13. Ghungroo
14. Pakhavaj

37. And the Oscar Goes To ...

								*											
								S	A	D	G	A	T	I					
					B	A	L	A											
								T	W	O									
						N	A	Y	A	K									
							K	A	P	U	R	U	S	H					
								J	A	L	S	A	G	H	A	R			
					T	H	E	I	N	N	E	R	E	Y	E				
						P	A	T	H	E	R	P	A	N	C	H	A	L	I
			T	H	E	W	O	R	L	D	O	F	A	P	U				
	A	S	H	A	N	I	S	A	N	K	E	T							
J	A	N	A	A	R	A	N	Y	A										

38. Strike a Tune

Bhangra — Bharatpur
Bhairavi — Dark
Darts — Darbari
Kalahari — Kalidasa
Kalyani — Hammer
Hammock — Hamsadhwani
Mall — Male
Malhar

All Creatures Great and Small

39. Jungle Adventure

R	H	I	N	O	C	E	R	O	S			I			S		G
E			I									N			N		H
D		B	L	U	E	S	H	E	E	P		D			O		A
P			G									I			W		R
A		N	I	L	G	A	I					A			L		I
N			R									N			E		A
D			I		S	A	M	B	A	R		B			O		L
A			T									I			P		
	B	L	A	C	K	B	U	C	K			S			A		
			H									O			R		
			R				P	Y	T	H	O	N			D		T
																	I
F	L	Y	I	N	G	S	Q	U	I	R	R	E	L				G
																	E
H	I	M	A	L	A	Y	A	N	B	L	A	C	K	B	E	A	R

40. Spot the Tiger

1. Bandipur National Park
2. Dudhwa National Park
3. Simlipal National Park
4. Namdapha National Park
5. Kanha National Park
6. Bandhavgarh National Park
7. Corbett National Park
8. Ranthambore National Park
9. Sundarbans National Park
10. Kaziranga National Park
11. Mudumalai National Park
12. Sariska National Park
13. Pakhui Tiger Reserve
14. Pench Tiger Reserve
15. Dampa Tiger Reserve

Food for Thought

41. On the Menu

1. Jammu and Kashmir – Roganjosh
2. West Bengal – Sandesh
3. Rajasthan – Dal Bati Churma
4. Punjab – Sarson ka Saag
5. Assam – Masor Jhol
6. Gujarat – Shrikhand
7. Maharashtra – Pooran Poli
8. Andhra Pradesh – Bisi Bele Huli Anna
9. Nagaland – Kelhe
10. Uttar Pradesh – Nargisi Kofta

42. The Spice of Life

1. Nutmeg
2. Fennel
3. Ginger
4. Saffron
5. Cinnamon
6. Clove
7. Pepper
8. Chilli
9. Cumin
10. Mustard
11. Carom
12. Coriander
13. Poppy
14. Fenugreek
15. Garlic

43. Vegetable Market

1. Abohar / Artichoke
2. Ayodhya / Yam
3. Darbhanga / Garlic
4. Quilon / Onion
5. Bhilwara / Radish
6. Dholka / Kale
7. Shimla / Lady's Finger
8. Dewas / Asparagus
9. Jammu / Mushroom
10. Madanapalle / Leeks
11. Rishikesh / Shallots
12. Hubli / Lima beans

44. Crop Matters

R	T	C	T	U	N	O	C	O	C
E	U	A	E	J	S	O	A	O	I
G	N	B	A	U	T	E	F	G	R
N	A	H	B	T	T	F	L	I	E
I	C	C	O	E	E	R	O	D	M
G	E	N	O	E	R	P	O	N	R
R	R	C	A	S	H	E	W	I	U
A	A	S	O	C	C	A	B	O	T
M	E	N	A	C	R	A	G	U	S
S	E	S	A	M	E	Z	I	A	M

Answer: Cash Crops

All Things Indian

45. National Identity

1. Peacock
2. Mango
3. Lotus
4. Banyan
5. Jana Gana Mana
6. Hockey
7. Tiger

Theme of the puzzle: NATIONAL SYMBOLS

46. Mind Your Language

Bengali, Oriya, Tamil, Sindhi, Marathi—Brahmi

Gujarati, Urdu, Kannada, Telugu, Khasi, Konkani—Grantha

47. Tribal Themes

Sand, Sanskrit, Santhals
Gondola, Gong, Gonds
Chef, Cheap, Chenchu
Bangles, Banana, Banjara
Munch, Mundane, Munda

48. Mining for Treasure

Aluminium, Cobalt, Copper, Coal, Diamond, Gold, Graphite, Iron Ore, Uranium, Zinc

49. Sparkling Stones

T	O	U	R	M	A	L	I	N	E	G	L
N	B	Q	T	O	P	A	Z	N	T	A	Y
A	S	U	S	A	R	D	I	U	I	R	R
I	I	A	**K**	**O**	**L**	R	R	O	T	N	E
L	D	R	**A**	**R**	T	Q	**G**	N	A	E	B
E	I	T	**O**	I	U	**L**	**D**	Y	M	T	D
N	A	Z	C	O	R	A	L	X	E	L	I
R	N	L	I	R	E	B	M	A	A	E	A
A	**M**	S	R	J	A	D	E	R	H	N	M
C	E	**I**	C	A	T	S	E	Y	E	I	O
L	O	L	I	T	E	M	**N**	**E**	**S**	P	N
R	U	B	Y	R	E	P	S	A	J	S	D

Answer: Kolar Gold Mines

50. Win-win Situation

1. Durand
2. Chadha
3. Ranji
4. Narang
5. Rovers
6. Duleep
7. Holkar
8. Vittal
9. Burdwan
10. Deodhar
11. Santosh
12. Gurmeet
13. Agarwal
14. Beighton
15. Subroto